An *EARLY* I CAN READ Book

WHAT HAVE I GOT?

by MIKE McCLINTOCK

Pictures by Leonard Kessler

Harper & Row, *Publishers*, New York and Evanston

What have I got?

I have a lot.

In my pocket I have a lot.

Do you want to see?

Look at me.

I have a box

Of rocks.

What is this thing?

Some string.

And look!

A hook!

That is not all.

I have a ball.

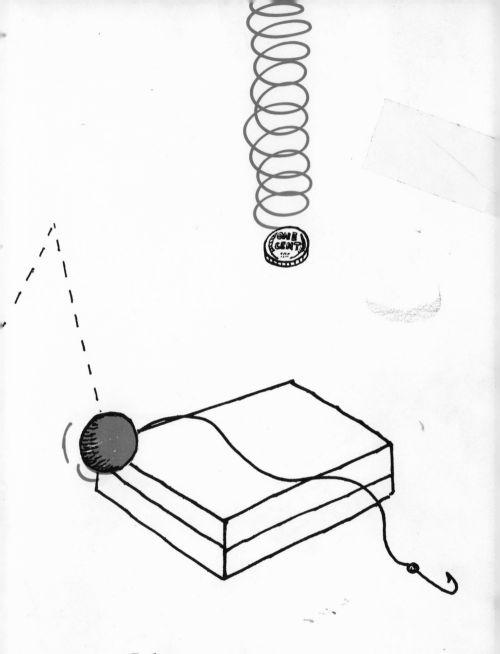

I have a penny.

Do you have any?

9

This is good—

A bit of wood.

I bet you wish

You had this dish.

11

Can I find more? I can.

This pan.

At last—my car!

And there we are.

Look at the things that I have got!

With things like this I can do a lot.

14

I shut my eyes—

And what a surprise!

With my penny I get candy.

This is dandy!

ARCADIA ELEMENTARY SCHOOL
ARCADIA INDIANA

With my ball I have some fun.

I hit a home run!

In my car

I can go far.

20

With my hook I get a fish,

22

If I wish.

I make a fire with my wood.

That is good.

In my pan I cook the fish.

Then I eat it from my dish.

I find a fox.

And as I put it in the box,

A bad man comes to take my rocks.

For they are gold,

So I am told.

I stop the bad man—look and see!

With string I tie him to a tree.

You can do lots of things, too,

If you

Have some things in your pocket.

Boy! What if I had a rocket?